Little Squiggle's Lake Adventure

By Laura Smetana and Stirling Hebda

Illustrated by Laura Smetana

Flying Cardinal Press, LLC

Library of Congress Control Number: 2021909868
ISBN: 978-1-7371409-1-7 (hardcover)
ISBN: 978-1-7371409-3-1 (paperback)
ISBN: 978-1-7371409-0-0 (e-book)
First Edition, August 2021
Cover and book design by Kath Grimshaw
Edited by Veronica Benduski and Meredith Tennant
Text set in True Sketch
The artwork in this book was created with watercolor and digital ink.

To my parents, who inspired a spirit of adventure, and Greg, for getting a kayak without asking (thank you)

—L.S.

To Shirley, for inspiring us to start watercoloring

—S.H.

"What should we do today?" Little Lou asked her best friend, Little Squiggle.

"Let's go to the lake!"
said Little Squiggle.
"We can try out my
new kayak."

Little Lou had never been kayaking before.
"Will there be sharks in the water?" she
asked as they walked to the lake.

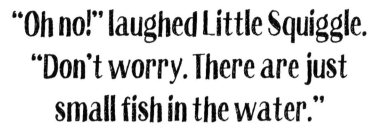

"Oh no!" laughed Little Squiggle. "Don't worry. There are just small fish in the water."

They climbed into the kayak and
paddled away from the shore.

Soon, shimmering water
surrounded them on all sides.

They paused to enjoy the view as they bobbed up and down on the choppy waves.

As the water calmed, Little Squiggle shouted, "Look! There's an island! Let's get closer to see the flowers."

"I'd love to," replied Little Lou.

Together, Little Squiggle and Little Lou paddled closer to the little island.

As they neared the island,
they saw flowers, bees,
and butterflies dancing in
the breeze.

In the clear blue water below, they saw
fish gliding between the seaweed,
while dragonflies
hummed above.

"Do you hear that beautiful music?"
asked Little Lou with a smile.

Little Squiggle paused for a moment and closed his eyes. "I think it's coming from that other island with trees," he said. "Let's go see what it is!"

The music grew louder and louder as they paddled closer and closer to the rocky shore. They came to a stop as the kayak scraped across the gravel below.

"Come on!" said Little Squiggle. "Let's explore the island to find out who is singing that beautiful song." "I'm not so sure," whispered Little Lou. "What about the kayak? We can't just leave it here."

"I have an idea!" said Little Squiggle. "We could use this rope." Little Squiggle tied one end of the rope to the kayak and placed three heavy rocks securely on the other end.

Afraid of falling in the
water, Little Lou took a
deep breath and slowly
stepped onto shore with
Little Squiggle's help. They
began to explore the island
to find out where the
music had come from.

They found rocks covered in green algae,

beautiful flowers blowing in the breeze,

graceful feathers from island birds,

and large, twisted pieces of metal.

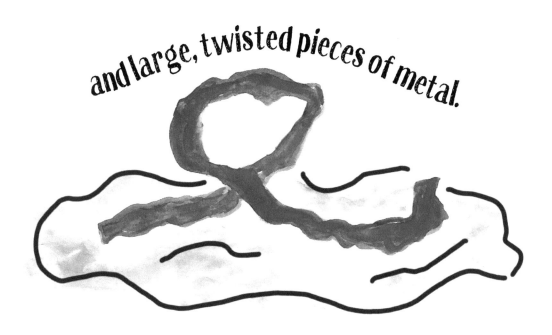

But no signs of music.

"Let's get a closer look," replied Little Squiggle. Step by step, they climbed up the hill to admire the unusual flower.

Suddenly, a little red bird landed on the flower and started singing the beautiful song they had heard from the shore.

When the little red bird finished
singing, Little Squiggle and Little Lou
clapped in admiration.
"Welcome to our island!" chirped the little red
bird. "Follow me and I'll show you around."

The little red bird gave Little Squiggle and Little Lou a tour of the island. They went up, down, and all around until they had seen every tree, rock, and flower. Then it began to drizzle.

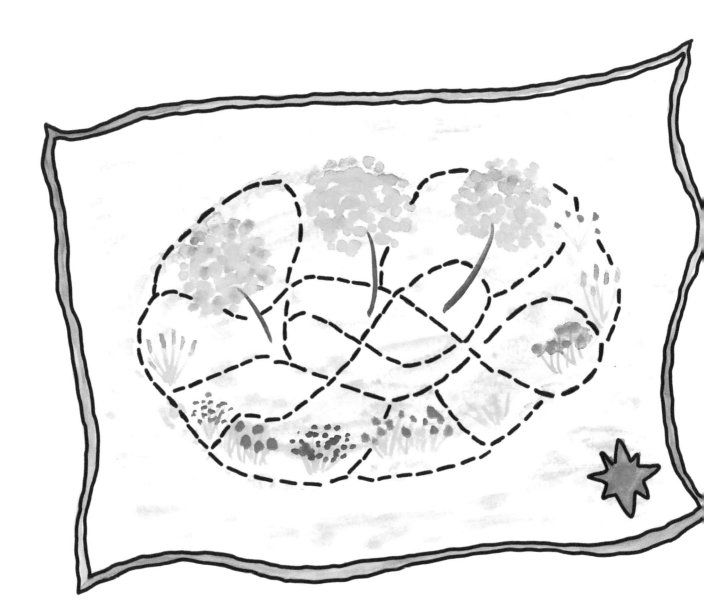

"Thank you for the tour," said Little Lou,
"but we should get going before it
starts to rain even more."
"Of course!" tweeted the little red bird.
"It was my pleasure. I'll take you
back to your kayak."

Little Squiggle and Little Lou's new friend led them back to the shore, but when they got there, the kayak was gone!

"Oh no! It's in the middle of the lake!"
cried Little Lou with panic in her voice.
"How are we going to get it back?"
"I can help!" said the little red bird,
zipping up into the trees.

Little Squiggle and Little Lou
stood frozen, their hearts
racing, as they watched
the kayak drift farther
and farther away.

With a whoosh of air, the little red bird
returned with a flock of feathered friends
speeding behind him.

The birds flew over the water, dodging raindrops that poured from the sky. Together, they grasped the rope tightly with their feet and pulled the kayak back across the water.

As soon as the birds brought
the rope close enough, Little
Squiggle and Little Lou grabbed
hold and helped the birds
pull the kayak up onto the
rocky shore.

"We did it! Thank you! Thank you!" cheered
Little Squiggle and Little Lou.
They hurried into the kayak and waved
goodbye to their new friends. Together,
they paddled back as fast as they
could, while the rain drenched
them from head to toe.

By the time they made it back to shore, the rain had stopped. The sun was shining and a beautiful rainbow filled the sky.

Little Lou and Little Squiggle couldn't wait
for their next adventure together!

About the Author-Illustrator

Laura Smetana loves writing, painting, and kayaking with her family. As a kid, Laura was a self-described bookworm, and one of her favorite places is still the library. In the fifth grade, Laura created a book about a giraffe named Little Squiggle. After reading it to Stirling for bedtime, he said, "We should bring Little Squiggle back, Mom!" And that's what they did. This is their first book together. You can visit her at **www.laurasmetana.com.**

About the Author

Stirling Hebda is Laura's son and is still a kid. He enjoys playing video games, freeze tag, and sports, like soccer and rugby. When he isn't at school, Stirling loves eating snacks and competing in enthusiastic rock-paper-scissors battles to get the best seat in the kayak. He lives with his parents and robot dog and cat.

CPSIA information can be obtained
at www.ICGtesting.com
Printed in the USA
BVHW021914290821
615541BV00006B/183